MELANIN
What Makes Black People Black!
(Biochemical Blackness)

Llaila Afrika

- ❖ How to protect it
- ❖ How to nourish Melanin
- ❖ Difference between Black and White People
- ❖ How it causes emotional behaviors and thoughts
- ❖ How it is being destroyed

Melanin
Copyright © 2009 by Llaila Afrika
address:
Seaburn Publishing Group
P.O. Box 2085
Long Island City, N.Y. 11102

Library of Congress Cat. Num.-in-Publication Data

2009 Afrika, Llaila

ISBN 1592321860 (paperback)

Available online:
www.blackbookplus.com

FOREWORD

The subject of Melanin is straight forward and simple to explain. Melanin is the biochemical substance that drives physical, mental, emotional and spiritual life. What makes the subject difficult to explain is the awkward primitive Latin Language that is used in Science. Any attempt to avoid the use of the Latin Language of chemistry and biology makes information appear unscientific and unintelligent, this was the challenge in writing about melanin, having to write in every day language and trying to avoid science Latin Jargon.

The lectures and books on melanin are very Latin jargon centered. Most Black people that read about melanin say "what good is it, it does not help you to be free." They of course are correct. A Black person is unaware of Melanin is manipulated and controlled by their unawareness. Black people need to know the basics about melanin and how to nourish melanin so they can get some positive use from it. Black people are controlled by their failure to realize that the Black race is a Melanin Dominate race. The key to controlling Black People is to reduce their Blackness (Melanin usage and knowledge). This will reduce their very ability to be Black which will directly affect their ability to be human and seek

4

what is humanly theirs – FREEDOM. Black people are a race nourishing themselves as if they are Caucasians. Since the Caucasians have the least amount of Melanin, then Black people that eat as if they are Caucasians are giving themselves the least amount of nourishment to their Melanin. This causes them to utilize their Melanin the least. Therefore, Black people are nutritionally against their own Melanin and anti-melanin. They are ignorantly fighting against Melanin and themselves. In this writing I have briefly attempted to reveal Melanin's properties and how the human body bio-chemically uses and nourishes it.

The Black race's under-education, dys-education (dysfunctional) and mis-education about Melanin merely reflects one particle of their white domination and post traumatic colonialism trauma and post traumatic slavery trauma. Black people must "know thyself" and to know yourself is to know Melanin.

ABOUT PINEAL AND MELANIN

The scientific literature has very few objective facts and many, many science principles and rules are subjective fairy tale stories called theory. All theories are unproven and unscientific. The objective facts are that Black people are a race that has the highest amount of the biochemical pigment called Melanin. Melanin is a civilizing chemical, reproduces itself, a free radical protector, can be transformed in the blood, concentrates nerve and brain information, neutralizes, oxidizes (breakdown) converts substances, reduces (builds) another substance and is unchanged by radiation and high temperatures. Melanin is inside and outside the body. The more melanin a race has the more humane and civilized the race. Science myths (theory) have clouded and avoided the true information about Melanin and the Pineal Gland that secretes Melanin.

Melanin is the vital chemical that makes life itself. It is usually brown to Black in color. Melanin is a flexible like plastic, can resemble a cloud, gas, wood, metal or liquid and takes on many forms without losing its structure. It is heat resistant, can endure temperatures of 1225°F, has a pleasant odor, resists x-ray diffraction, resist strong acids and alkaline, etc. Melanin is found in the environment, springs, lakes, soil, plants, atmosphere and animals.

The pituitary gland which is a gland in the middle of the brain that secretes growth hormones has been erroneously called the master gland. However, the Pineal Gland which is also in the middle of the brain is the true master gland. The Pineal Gland secretes Melanin which regulates all bodily functions and glands (cycles, circadian rhythms) in the body. Melanin is a biochemical that has a high molecular weight. This means it has many functions and links like a chain that contains carbon-nitrogen, ether, saturated carbon-carbon, unsaturated carbon-carbon, organometallic, peroxides and is essentially a Black carbon hydro amine. These various links allows melanin to be a polymer (takes many forms) and polycyclic (many rhythms) and have a unique property and flexible chemical ability.

Melanin is made by cells called Melanocytes. Inside the Melanocytes are smaller organs (organelle) called Melanosome which make melanin. Inside the Endoplasmic Reticulum the Melanosomes are made. In other words, small cells build bigger cells, bigger cells build larger cells and the end product of all the building from a small particle into a larger particle is the chemical Melanin.

Melanin essentially produces itself with substances such as copper. Melanin absorbs all types of energy such as sunlight, electromagnetic, music heard by the human ear and sounds the human ear cannot hear, phone waves, radio waves, radar, computer radiation, x-ray, cosmic rays, ultraviolet rays, heat waves, microwaves, etc. Melanin uses the energy in the total environment such as water energy, earth, moon, sun, galaxy, cycles of planets, cycles of planets, cycles of minerals etc. On the molecular level the melanin particles called electrons, protons, neutrons and solatons rearrange their orbits. This is called resonance. In other words, the melanin particles vibrate and rearrange themselves to fill the weak (low) energy sites. Resonance causes a particle to move, this movement causes a small gap (low energy) site and the other particles rearrange themselves to (double bond shift) fill the gap.

Melanin is the natural chemical that makes Black people's skin Black. It is present in Black people's bodies, skin, cells, nerves, brain, muscles, bones, reproductive and digestive systems and all bodily functions in a higher amount than all other races.

Melanin is a biological active substance of various size cells. It is made of nutrients such as indoles, histamines, phenylalanine, catecholamines (norepinephrine, epinephrine, dopamine, etc.) and the amino acid tyrosine. Melanin is made of various attached parts called chains which are linked to unsaturated carbon-carbon, saturated carbon-carbon, carbon-nitrogen, organometallic, ether. peroxides and quinine which are brown to Black in color. Chemicals such as Flavin, Pteridines, Flavonoid, Napthquinone, Polycyclicquinone, Anthraquinone, Phenoxazones, convert into Melanin (polymerize or co-polymerize).

The color of melanin appears as Black because it is absorbing all colors. Once the color enters the melanin it cannot escape. Melanin is concentrated colors, it is a cellular Black Hole similar to the Black Holes in outer space. The human eye only sees colors that are reflected away from an object. If an object appears Black in color, that means that the object is absorbing all colors except Black. Black is reflected away from the object, consequently, you see Black. Black is a pigment (color) that makes carbon Black in appearance.

MELANIN

Melanin is an organic dark carbon chemical pigment substance. Melanin gives Black peoples eyes iris a brown color and gives the dark color to their hair, skin and the Substantia Nigra of the brain. This is an area of the brain where the cerebrum connects to the pons.

Melanin is secreted by the Pineal Gland. The Pineal Gland has a pine cone shape, is reddish in color and the stem of it is approximately half an inch in length and the head of it is slightly smaller than a green pea and the total weight is about two grams. The Pineal Gland consist of nerve cells similar to those in the retina nerve of the eye. The retina nerve is inside the eyeball and receives light stimulation which it transmits to the brain. The Pineal Gland is found inside a fluid filled space inside the middle of the brain called the third ventricle and it is attached inside the ventricle.

The Pineal stimulates the growth of the nervous system's cerebrum (thinking brain part called gray matter). Therefore, an under-stimulated Pineal in childhood can decrease thinking ability in adulthood. The Melanin content of the nerves is highest in Black People. Melanin allows nerve messages to travel fast without resistance causing super conductivity. Black people have the highest amount of Melanin on the upper part of the spinal cord (brain stem) where the lower part of the brain connects to the spinal cord. The Melanin concentrates on the brains Locus Ceruleus in the 4th ventricle and Reticular Formation (Black dots). This causes the brain to store more information and function at a high level. The function of the body's Melanin and the brain's Melanin is reduced by steroids (cortical adrenals), stimulants (synthetic speeds, cocaine, caffeine), anti-depressants (anti-cholinergics) and unnatural light.

The Pineal helps to regulate the hypothalamus glands release factors that stimulate the Pituitary to secrete the Follicle Stimulating Hormone (FSH) and aides the Luteinizing Hormone (LH). FSH stimulates the ovaries and the movement of sperm and LH stimulates egg and sperm production. Consequently, a Black person with an under-stimulated Pineal or one that uses drugs or eats processed (junk food) foods will harm the Pineal and have reproductive problems.

The processed foods and drugs impact the Pineal. The Pineal regulates insulin levels, the adrenal cortex and the Adrenocorticotropic Hormone (ACTH). ACTH is secreted by the Pituitary and is essential for physical and mental growth and development. In other words, a Black person's level of thinking (mental growth) needed to solve their race's problems cannot be achieved with a low amount of Melanin caused by an under-stimulated Pineal.

The melanin secreted by the Pineal aides the posterior pituitary's effect on the hormone Oxytocin. Oxytocin stimulates uterine contraction during the birth of a baby. Oxytocin is similar to morphine, it is one of the main hormones that causes people to bond to each other (mother and child, man and woman, friends with friends). Black people with inadequate Melanin levels will have problems getting along together (unity, forming positive groups) and will constantly destroy each other. They will lack the energy to sustain unity because natural bodily made sugars regulated by melanin cannot be utilized. This is the result of inadequate insulin. The Pancreas insulin hormone takes the natural sugars (not white sugar etc.) out of the blood and puts it into tissue. The Melanin's inability to regulate insulin causes mood swings, irritability and low energy. The liver's ability to make bile is potentiated by Melanin. The Pineal's Melanin hormones act on the liver and if inadequate, this will decrease the gall bladder's digestive bile fluid secretion. This results in unstable energy and moods. The Pineal stimulates the nervous system and the brain. Consequently, brain function is compromised and the type of thinking needed to create ideas to solve emotional, mental and spiritual problems is not sufficient.

The Pineal Glands ability to secrete Melanin is sunlight dependant. The sun radiates full color spectrums of light. Full spectrum light striking the eyes' retina nerve stimulates the Pineal Gland to secrete Melanin. Melanin turns into serotonin hormone and melatonin hormone. Black people that spend vast amounts of time indoors and out of sunlight or are exposed to the visual pollution of artificial light, sunglasses, television, reflected light of concrete, bricks, highways and buildings, window glass, contact lens, monitors, television screens and fluorescent lights, wireless cell phones, ear phones and cars tend to have mild depression. A polluted environment, public drinking water, noise pollution, negative moods or social situations, acidic bodily conditions, lack of exercise, processed foods, synthetic drugs and computers decrease melanin production and the stimulation of the Pineal. This visual pollution can result in mild depression because the Pineal Gland is deprived of sunlight and exposed to negative stimulation.

When children are deprived of sunlight it can cause physical and emotional problems. Children who spend many hours indoors (school buildings), playing video games, viewing television and using artificial light are deprived of sunlight. Sunlight deprivation results in an under-stimulated Pineal causing the child to grow up and become an adult with decreased reproductive function (decrease gonad weight). In adult animals that have no reproductive organ (gonad) due to castration, the Pineal gets small and the pituitary gets large. Sunlight deprivation decreases the stimulation of the Pineal (almost similar to a castration state condition) which causes one to conclude that the same effect happens with people = Pineal shrinks and pituitary enlargement. The under-stimulated Pineal decreases (inhibits) the reproductive organs (gonads) response to Gonadotrophins. This causes a decrease weight of the ovaries and testicles. The Pineal gland increases sperm production and helps with female fertility. The Pineal gland increases progesterone hormone (made by the Corpus Luteum). Also the Pineal's melanin secretions help produce melatonin.

Melatonin is the hormone that synchronizes the rhythmaticity of the body. It helps to control the circadian rhythm. The body has a circadiam (cycle) rhythm for digesting food. Food ideally should be eaten from 12 noon to 7pm, metabolized into the blood from 7pm to 4am and from 4am to noon the body is cleansing. The Pineal gland secretion of melanin converts into serotonin then melatonin. These hormones need darkness and sunlight to stabilize the rhythm of the body. Sunlight deprivation destabilizes the circadian rhythm causing Seasonal Affective Disorder (SAD). This is associated with abnormal melatonin activity. SAD depression symptoms can be relieved with daily exposure to sunlight and to full spectrum artificial light bulbs and the use of melatonin supplement.

Melatonin supplements along with optimum nutrition, adequate darkness and sunlight are vital. Melatonin release is stimulated by Noradrenaline (norephinephrine), low blood sugar (hypoglycemia), darkness and Dopamine. The addition of a Melatonin supplement helps Dopamine to calm the emotions and body, helps tryptophan to make serotonin, helps stop antibodies produced by corticosteroids, decreases the growth of certain types of cancers, causes sedation and sleep and decreases the growth of tumors. Melatonin is dependant upon melanin and melanin is dependant upon the Pineal gland and healthy nutrition (whole unprocessed, unchemicalized foods).

MELANIN HORMONES

The Pineal Gland makes alkaloids. An alkaloid is an organic (means contains carbon) substance that reacts to salts. A salt in chemistry is a chemical compound that is created when an acid and alkaline substance interact. A salt has a positive charged electrical element other than Hydroxyl (commonly called acid) because the alkaloids react to salt that uses them. Salts are used in the body to maintain stable nerves, water balance, regulate the blood volume, are essential for digestion enzymes, hormones, control thickness of the blood (coagulation), pressure inside cells (osmotic), respiratory pigments and acid-base balance. This means that melanin hormones are the primary controller of human life itself. The salts referred to are not table salt chemically known as the poison sodium chloride (chloride is a type of bleach) but the salt of sulfates, phosphates, chloride, carbonates, bicarbonates which are combined with calcium, magnesium and potassium.

The alkaloid serotonin hormone is stimulated by sunlight and full spectrum artificial light. It is secreted into the blood during day light hours. Serotonin connects to other substances (polymerizes) and forms into melanin. It causes muscles to contract, blood vessels to constrict, regulates blood pressure and has the ability to alter consciousness (improvise other realities). Consequently, the heighten ability to create spontaneously (improvise) is a characteristic of Black peoples music (i.e. jazz), dance, acting, dress styles, hair styles, language usage, inventions, science, art and culture.

The alkaloid Melatonin is made by the Pineal Gland. It is secreted into the blood after sunset and reaches its highest levels around 10pm. This alkaloid connects to other substances (polymerizes) and forms melanin. It helps maintain, repair and build brain and nerve tissue. Consequently, it is good for all brain and nerve damage diseases such as Lupus, Alzheimers, Attention Deficient (a form of Senility), Parkinson, Senility, Memory Loss, Numbness and Tingling of nerves. Melanin synchronizes body functions, helps to maintain the circadian rhythm, stimulates secretion of milk and contractions of the uterus, triggers puberty, increases electrical brain wave activity, regulates blood pressure, induces sleep, stimulates improvising and gives a positive effect on emotions and creates a feeling of well being and joy.

The alkaloids serotonin and melatonin contain a similar structure as other alkaloids. It is the aromatic benzene structure and amino groups that cause the melanin hormones to easily chemically merge with dangerous drugs such as crack, Ritalin, cocaine, caffeine, codeine morphine, mescaline, etc. Black people with their higher melanin content are twice as addicted to synthetic drugs than other races. White Domination which uses the myth of White Supremacy defended by White Racism have created and maintain the physical, mental, emotional, spiritual, global, social and cultural oppression of Black people. This causes Black people to take drugs, use sex, violence, white sugar, gambling and abuse of each other to emotionally and psychologically escape the oppressive condition. A social condition created by White Domination that causes Black people to socially, emotionally and physically kill themselves is by definition Genocide. The drugs kill and have an effect on the mind and the physical body of Black people –which means they act upon melanin. The drugs are anti-melanin and against Black culture. The many substances which are made from melanin are good in the correct concentration (i.e. alkaloids) and ratios.

Alkaloids are organic nitrogen substances which are destructive (corrosive) metallic hydroxides (ammonium, carbonates). When alkaloids are made by the human body they are not harmful because they are at the correct proportion and concentrations. The Pineal gland makes the unharmful alkaloid serotonin and melatonin. Aside from this, the body makes many toxic chemicals at the correct unharmful concentration such as alcohol, ammonia, bleach (hydrochloric acid), lye (sulfuric acid) etc. However, when synthetic (man-made) chemicals are consumed they bond and incorporate themselves into melanin and generate harmful chemical species that can attack the body at any given moment. This attack can be stimulated by normal body activity as well as negative emotions and social activities. Melanin dominate Black people are highly susceptible to these attacks because they consume synthetic chemicalized junk foods, beverages, drugs and cosmetics. These chemical reactions are related to Melanin dominate Black people, who do not know they have studied Melanin.

Melanin is studied in chemistry which is the study of Keme (Black melanin particles) called protons, electrons, neutrons and solatons. However, the word melanin is never mentioned in European (Greek) chemistry. Melanin is studied in biology because the purplish (melaninated) brain of the cell called the nucleus is studied. However, the word Melanin is never mentioned. Melanin is the chemical key to life and the brains (nucleus) of all cells. In order for information to be transported to the brain it must be in a liquid form. You see, hear, smell, taste, touch and feel life with your brain (melanin). Therefore, what eyes see, ears hear, tongue tastes, and nose smells; these sensations are converted into a liquid in order to get to the brain. The chemical of conversion or change is melanin. It allows you to be in contact with your inner body and allows your body to be in contact with life itself. The Black race has the highest amount of melanin and has the highest contact with inner life (emotions, spiritual, subconscious, sublime and extrasensory life).

Melanin comes in many varieties and has multiple functional properties. A synthetic drug alters the functional properties of melanin. A synthetic drug that does not act upon melanin is not a drug. A synthetic drug must speed up, slow down, stop or either destroy melanin to be a drug. Any of the body's natural chemical substances or symbiotic virus, bacteria or flora that is outside its range of positive usefulness in the body is un-useful. When it is labeled un-useful it is given names such as free radical, toxin, harmful, parasite, worms and bacterial, viral, fungus and yeast infection. The body's natural chemical substances, bacteria, virus, fungus and yeast can become out of positive usefulness from taking anti-melanin synthetic chemicals, drugs, processed and chemicalized junk foods, negative emotions and behaviors and a polluted physical and social environment. Melanin acts and reacts upon chemicals.

Melanin has a free radical behavior. It will attack harmful synthetic chemicals (i.e. preservatives, food additives, drugs, cocaine, crack, Viagra, caffeine) and attach to them in an attempt to transport them elsewhere or neutralize them. The harmful chemical incorporates into the structure of melanin (copolymerize). The harmful chemical and melanin become one molecule. This combined melanin and harmful chemical molecule is lodge throughout the body. Emotional stress, disease, physical stressors, junk food, cell phone and computer radiation and drugs can cause the release of this combined melanin and harmful chemical molecule into the blood and into interactions with other chemicals, hormones, minerals and nutrients. The combined melanin and harmful chemical accumulates in the body and can cause a toxic overdose, it can breakdown (depolymerize) or reincorporate (polymerize).

Black people's cells have the highest melanin content. Cells build tissue and tissues make organs, organs make organ systems and organ systems constitute the body. The cell has an outer skin (membrane). The cell membrane has a bone type structure called microfilaments, microtubes (cytoskeleton) and hair like antenna. The antenna senses the liquid environment outside the cell (extra cellular matrix). Melanin is the chemical that converts information outside and inside the cell. Liquid information such as nutrients, red blood cells, white blood cells, fats, enzymes, proteins and hormones need to be constantly read by the melanin. The melanin is the body's computer in a liquid form. It breaks down substances into small units (depolymerazations) and builds small units into larger substances (polymerizations). The information (data) travels on the neurological information highway (Reticular Formation) and is put on a monitoring screen of the brain (Melanin Reticular Formation) and is read by the brain's Frontal Cortex. Information comes from the nerves to the spinal cord to the top of the brain stem to the medulla oblongata to the pods to the cerebellum to the cerebrum. The information highway can have traffic jams, blocks and detours caused by synthetic drugs, junk foods, toxic emotions, feelings and spiritual distortions. The information highway (neurological pathway) problems can create a Black person that is culturally homeless and seeking to serve European culture.

Melanin has effects upon Black people's social behavior and has an effect inside the body.

Melanin is highly concentrated in the gastrointestinal tract of the digestive system, vagina, uterus, penis, sperm storage sac (seminal vesicle), ear (auditory nerves), eye (retina, iris), nervous system, etc, The synthetic drugs enter into the blood stream and are carried all over the body. They are absorbed and interact with melanin in various local areas. These drugs combine (polymerizes) and form different chemicals similar to hybridizing the cells. The cells in local areas resonate or readjust to the synthetic chemical. This creates a type of freak cell similar to genetic modification invaders of the cell. The end result of this biological war fare done by synthetic social drugs and prescription drugs has not been calculated. Black people using illegal (crack) and legal (caffeine, alcohol, nicotine) drugs are a walking experiment with unknown results. It is not a matter of **if** Black people will get sick and manifest more physical, mental and spiritual diseases, it is a matter of **when** they will get sick. Parents that eat junk foods and consume drugs will birth chemically altered children.

The main example of the destruction caused by synthetic drugs are the female's eggs. For example, an adult woman that is pregnant with a girl can damage the girl's eggs. A pregnant woman taking drugs, marijuana and/or alcohol, their immune system can fight the physiological effect. Despite the immune system's attempt to protect itself from the drug the pregnant woman will get high. The baby girl that she is pregnant with can fight the effect of the drug. However, the unborn baby girl will get high. All unborn girls have all the eggs they will ever have before they are born. Unborn girls do not grow eggs after they are born; they are born with their lifetime supply. The unborn girl's eggs have no immune system. The synthetic drugs have a direct effect on her eggs. The melanin in the eggs and ovaries connects to the drugs (polymerizes) forming a type of mental, physical and spiritual genetic alteration. Simply put, the pregnant woman is chemically cloning a Black person. The man's sperm has no immune system and the synthetic drugs has a polymerizing effect on it. The man's sperm becomes an alter sperm and in many ways becomes a freak sperm looking for a chemicalized freak egg that will birth freak children searching for White Supremacy to serve and worship. Melanin's healthy impact upon Black people, is good and melanin that is altered or damaged has a bad effect upon Black people.

A Black person's emotions and behaviors can be anti-melanin by adopting Caucasian culture as their primary or only culture. African cultural adultery is anti-melanin and is typical of Black people that have no African cultural practices and seek or maintain ways to serve or entertain Caucasians, practice Caucasian types of relationships and sex. They eat Caucasian processed chemicalized junk foods. Anti-melanin Black people have a lifestyle that allows them to be off their cultural whole foods (unprocessed) diet, which means they are off their culture. They are anti-melanin and out of their culture, out of their natural whole food diet and essentially out of their mind and into the Caucasian mind. Negative anti-melanin thoughts, states of consciousness, moods, as well as synthetic drugs cause electrons (minerals with an electrical charge) in melanin to go from a stable state to an excited unstable state. This results in DNA genetic damage, and abnormal psychological states and physical illnesses. The negative unstable excited melanin state can cause toxic chemicals (species) that may result in the destruction of melanin and physical diseases. Melanin attaches to synthetic chemicals as a way to grab them and eject them out of the system. However, the continuous consumption of the synthetic chemicals over saturates and spills the chemical into the blood stream harming everything with a high melanin content (i.e. brain, sex organs, digestion). In fact, synthetic chemicals eaten get absorbed by the melanin in the digestive system , then go to the brain and sex organs. The digestive system dumps synthetic chemicals from the intestines into the liver then circulate in the blood. Synthetic chemicals decrease the liver's immune response, storage of nutrients and absorption of nutrients such as tryptophan.

The amino acid tryptophan converts into serotonin which changes into melatonin. During the day serotonin increases while at night melatonin increases. Melatonin aides the growth and repair of tissue by controlling the cells ability to increase its oxygen content which creates intracellular anti-oxidants. A melanin deficiency causes tissue to destruct or rust (oxidize). Low melanin causes free radicals to damage tissue. Melatonin helps to control prostaglandins. Prostaglandins are a type of fatty acid found in the brain, pancreas, kidney, prostate, uterus, thymus and lungs. Some prostaglandins are similar to oxytocin and can cause reproductive problems when melatonin is low because of emotional, spiritual, physical or disease stressors. Stressors can activate cortisol and adrenocortical hormone (hydrocortisone) which suppresses the immunity. A suppressed immune system causes many diseases. Diseases have an effect on your mind, mood and state of consciousness.

Consciousness is a cultural element. The culture educates a person to have awareness and awareness gives consciousness. Cultures use music, clothes, foods, dance, text books, myths, stories, religion, folktales, art and science to create a society. The smallest unit of a society is the individual. The individual is the mirror of a culture. The culture gives a person a belief system and beliefs give a person emotions. A reaction to your emotion is called a feeling. A feeling that lasts a long time is called a mood. In other words, feelings are based upon culture. Consequently a Black person that hears Chinese culture's music will not instantly get up and dance because they have no feelings for that music. There is no cultural connection. A Black person that has been culturally castrated with Post Traumatic Slavery and/or Post Traumatic Colonialism traumas will have a distorted consciousness. Added to this, a junk food (under nutrition) diet will decrease melanin and this causes a decreased consciousness.

A Black person with under nutrition will have physical, social and mental problems. They willl probably need to take a melatonin supplement.

Melatonin Supplement:

- Helps dopamine to calm the body and brain. Dopamine helps nerves to communicate with each other. It stimulates the hypothalamus and pituitary to release Growth Hormone (GH). Dopamine is required for the ability to sleep, fat gain and loss, sex drive, bone density, energy, the brain centers immunity and bodily motor control.

- Helps antibodies make cortico steroids a hormone from the adrenal gland that influences digestion and helps the liver make storage sugar (glycogen).

- Helps tryptophan to make serotonin.

- Increases oxygen absorption and life expectancy.

- Helps alkaline the system.

- Helps mental illness.

The body will trigger Melatonin because of Noradrenaline (Norepinephrine), Low Blood Sugar (Hypoglycemia) and Dopamine. Melatonin is released as a reaction to a disease, emotional, spiritual, social or science crisis. A Caucasian science crisis is caused by faulty distorted information that uses European theories (myths).

The problem with understanding melanin is the sciences of Caucasians. Their sciences, contains many, many myths called theories. And their science is White Male Centered. For example, their belief (myth) in Evolution is founded upon the idea that society was formed because men went away from home to hunt for animals. The facts are men, women and children formed society. The hurting of animals in primitive societies is done with nets (large nets for elephants, small nets for rabbits, fish etc.) and nets are made by men, women and children. Society was not built upon the basis that man went off hunting. Hunting is a family affair. The foundation of psychology is based upon the behavior of a man called Oeidipus. Oeidipus is a boy in an ancient Greek fairy tale (myth) that physically lust for sex with his mother. He killed his father and his mother lust sexually for her son Oeidipus, and married him. The use of this Caucasian psychology has distorted a Black person's ability to think healthy and understand themselves.

Psychology's root word is Psyche. Psyche means butterfly. A butterfly has two wings., one wing represents good and the other wing evil. Consequently, good and evil are always at odds with each other, they are constantly fighting each other. If one moves the other moves to counter act the other's movement. The wings moving is believed to make the mind think. Add to this belief is the belief that there are 3 divisions to the brain. There is Id the animal brain, Ego that fights to control the animal brain with a human brain and Superego the mother and father (society) that fights to control the Ego human brain that is locked into a constant battle with the Id animal sexual lust brain. This Caucasian myth is the basis of their psychology and for Black people to use this myth to understand their mind or science presents too many problems. This myth points to the lack of ability of caucasians to reach higher levels of thought and physical function.

Caucasians lack the genetic ability to produce (catalyze) significan levels of the heavy molecular weight melanin called Eumelanin. Eumelanin has its highest content in Black people. Caucasians have a pseudomelanin (phaeomelanin). Their pseudomelanin (pseudo=not a true melanin) can cause their spirit, mind and body to function below an optimum level and cause them to tend to have many diseases and disorders of the spirit, mind and body. Black people with the Eumelanin can have the ability to manufacture and reproduce melanin by using sunlight, the amino acid tyrosine, the metal copper and perhaps compounds that use oxygen (peroxides) as a free radical. The Free radical use of oxygen allows it to break down substances. This is similar to using oxygen to rust (break down) metal. This gives Black people many different (improvisational) ways to utilize the chemical melanin and utilize spirit, mind and body.

HOW TO MEASURE MELANIN

There are many ways to measure melanin's biological, electromagnetic, hormone and chemical activities. The potential (p) for Hydrogen (H) which is called pH and the Blood Pressure can be used to test Melanin.

The pH is an electrical measurement of the saliva and urine. The saliva reflects the Autonomic Nervous System's Parasympathetic nerves actions and reactions. The urine reflects the Autonomic's Sympathetic activity.

The test of the pH of saliva and urine samples is done after the person has not eaten or drank fluids (includes water) for two hours, then the samples pH is read with color metric pH paper and the pH is recorded.

There are levels in which melanin can deviate from normal. Melanin can be insufficient or deficient. A melanin insufficiency can be caused when the supply of melanin can not meet the demand for melanin. The individual's body can demand excessive amounts of melanin to fight disease, air, water and noise pollution, radiation from computers and cell phones, synthetic drugs, social stress, negative relationship, emotional and spiritual stress. This high amount of demand can not be met by an individual that consumes drugs and eats junk foods and does not use herbal medicine and whole foods to defend the body. A melanin insufficiency is indicated when the urine pH is below or above the normal 6.4 pH of urine. A melanin insufficiency is indicated when the systolic Blood Pressure number of 120 is below or above the normal range. Note, the Blood Pressure norm value of 120/80 in which the top number of 120 is the systolic. The systolic number as well as urine pH is related to melanin's serotonin, the sympathetic nervous system, acidity, the usage of carbohydrates for energy, the left hemisphere of the brain, etc. (see Melanin energy classification).

A melanin deficiency is indicate when the saliva pH is below or above the normal 6.4 saliva pH range. A melanin deficiency is indicated when the diastolic Blood Pressure number is below or above the normal 80 range. Note, the Blood Pressure norm value of 120/80, the number 80 or bottom number is the diastolic. The diastolic number, as well as the saliva pH is related to melanin's melatonin, the parasympathetic nervous system, alkalinity, the usage of raw fats (i.e. nuts, seeds, avocado) the right hemisphere of the brain, etc. (see Melanin Energy Classification).

A melanin deficiency can be caused when there is an adequate supply of melanin and the body's ability to use the melanin is dysfunctional (deficient). The body's metabolic and nerve (neurological) path malfunctions because of a weaken liver, pancreas, kidney, nervous system, respiratory system, reproductive system and immune system. The liver can be damaged due to drugs, sodas, vinegar and alcohol. The pancreas primarily gets damaged due to process sugars and concentrated sweeteners. The kidneys get damaged from process sugars and the poison sodium chloride (table salt), high blood pressure and mineral congestion. The other bodily systems can be damaged by hormonal and gland problems that compromise the ability to utilize melanin. The malfunctioning organs, glands and hormones can not adequately process melanin. Therefore, it can be used by the body.

RACES OF HUMANS

Classification of races based upon melanin content inside the body and the skin.

TYPE	COLOR	RACE
6	Black, Blue/Black (Highest melanin content)	Africans
5	Black/Brown, Brown	Native Indians (Mexicans, Malaysians, kwk)
4	Brown, Red	Native Americans, Japanese
2 and 3	Yellow, mixed, mixed Brown	Orientals
1	White (lowest melanin content)	Caucasians

HEALTH STANDARDS

Medical laboratory normal values, daily recommended allowances of vitamins and minerals, therapeutic dosages of herbs and drugs, baby formulas, disease reactions, human growth and development schedules, brain activity and psychology are all based upon the melanin content of Caucasians. The laboratory and Scientific norm values have to be different for each race because each race is biochemically different. The laboratory standards test Black people as if they are White people, then declare Black people sick because Blacks do not meet White Standards. This is Medical White Racism.

ANATOMY
(Differences between the Black and White Races)

	BLACKS	WHITES
Melanin	Selenium Centered Melanin Higher Molecular Weight (Eumelanin)	Sulphur centered Melanin
	– high content in body	– Least amount- causing albinism
	– Increase color absorption in eyes	– Least ability
	– Increase sound absorption in ears	– Lower Molecular weight Pheomelanin (pseudomelanin)
	– Acts as polymer	
	– Converts energy	
	– Acts as a computer	
	– Controls cyclical rhythms of all organs	
	– Controls sleep	
	– Controls growth (rate of puberty)	
	– Reacts to gravity (electromagnetic forces)	
	– Highest storage of information	
	– Processes largest amount of information in mid brain	
	– Processes left mind thoughts in right and left hemispheres of brain.	
	– Processes right mind thoughts in left and right hemispheres of brain.	
	– Can taste the full range of flavor of foods due to melanin in cells.	
	– Can smell the true aromas has the broadest range of smell identification	
	– Highest psyche ability	
	– Absorbs most electromagnetic energy	
	– Highest civilizing ability	

due to high melanin
content
- Increase memory to
memory transfer of stored
information
- Process most information
in corpus colostrums
- Evolve highest spirituality
due to melanin content

Skin Melanin (Black Pigmentation)	- Allows protection from suns ultraviolet rays - Allows protection from extreme hot and cold temperatures	- Least of all races, causing white skin
Buttock (Stetobygia)	- High muscular development - Allows extensive hip and thigh movements	- Flat, limited mobility.
Legs	- Longer in proportion to upper body - Allows better movement for walking and running	- Short
Blood	- When heated (burnt) forms complex pyramids - Allows better storage and transmuting of energy	- Less pyramidal
Liver	- Slightly large - Allows increased cleansing and energy storage	- Slightly smaller.
Hair	- Least amount of body hair caused by heat insulating effect of melanin - Broadest color spectrum bands in hair	- The most hairy of all races
Hair type	- Curly and brown	- Flat and limp, weak

	– Allows quicker transmission and receiving of electrical and magnetic energy similar to an antenna – Hair shaped like galaxy (cross section shape)	antennas – Least color bands – Hair is closest to fur – Hair has a kidney shape, slightly divided appearance (cross section chape)
Alcohol	– Higher amount naturally made by body. Helps to cool body	– Lowest amount
Ammonia	– Lowest amount naturally made by body	– Highest amount, makes then slightly warm when in cold temperatures and problems in hot temperatures. – Sun can cause cancer.
Eyes	– Farthest apart – Allows increased field of vision (peripheral) – Eyes are brown, due to Melanin content. – Allows better reception of Sun's color light heat which results in higher stimulation of Pineal and pituitary glands. – Absorbs full color, can see the true color of objects.	– Closer together, narrow field of vision – Eyes blue, gray and green because veins are seen in back of eyes. – See paler colors.
Nose	– Broad and flat. – Allows angular contour to air columns causing it to vibrate at higher frequency, thus stimulating electromagnetic energy. – Allows wider field of vision for individual eye.	-Raised chiseled bridge blocks field of vision and separates and divides images (sees world divided) limited field of vision.

Women's physique	– "T" shape similar to mens', broad shoulder fossils indicate superior muscular structure. – Allows more independent muscular movements and counter balance for hips and pregnancy weight.	– No "T" shape, narrow shoulders, hips wider than shoulders, poor counterbalancing ability
Nerves	– High melanin content in nervous system. – Allows nerve messages to travel faster and protects against disease.	– Least amount of melanin of all races.
Jaw	– Wider arch – Indicates diet high in vegetables.	– Narrow, similar to flesh eating animals.
Sulphur	– Low amount	– High amount, gives offensive smell to hair when wet.
Salt	– Low amount.	– Retains waste in body. – High Amount
Arms	– Longer in proportion to body. – Allows better counter balancing	– Short, limit balancing ability
Lips	– Thick. – Allows wider face muscular field and better extraction of juices from plants. Act as sensor	– Thin
Voice	– Wider range of speech tones; high and low sounds – Melanin allows melodious and rhythmical speech	– Limited range with flat speech tones, tones have no rhythm, lacks melodious sounds.
Ears	– Small and stationary – Allows better center of sounds. – Fluid different in weight inside air	– Large- can move them.

Stomach	– Has the most flora (Fungi, Yeast and Bacteria that live in stomach, entire digestive tract, uterus, vagina, eyes, ears, etc). – Is specific and unique only to Blacks, have slightly more than 3 pounds – Allows food to be broken down (metabolized) at a greater nutritional level	– No vast variety of flora, limits food metabolism, Tends to have a worm population.
Vagina Lips	– Larger – Allows tighter seal and increases flora lifespan	– Smaller
Vaginal Shaft	– Longer – Allows increased muscular activity	– Short.
Penis	– Length slightly longer	– Shorter
Skull	– Sagittal contour flat (top of head).	– Round
Face height	– Low	– High
Eye	– Orbital opening rectangular.	– Angular
Nasal	– Opening Wide (nose).	– Narrow
Lower nasal margin	– Wide base	– Sharp
Facial profile	– Downward slant	– Straight, no slant.
Palate shape	– -Wide	– Narrow
Skin	– -Absorbs greatest percentage of colors	– Reflect colors
Color	– -Eyes darken with age	– Extremely rare
Sacral Spot	– -Birthmark on lower back	– Extremely rare

	and/or buttocks	
Breath	– Deeper (characteristic of right-minded thinking).	– Shallow breath. (Left-minded).
Skin	– Processes more Vitamin D (high amount owing to melanin.	– Poor processor of Vitamin D.
Calcium intake	– Lower (High amount of Vitamin D created by melanin stabilizes calcium, reduces need for high intake).	– High Calcium intake required.
Stemoclavicular muscle	– Allows mobility for swinging from one tree limb to another similar to monkeys; rare.	– Found abundantly
Pores of Skin	– Widen with age	– No change
Muscle	– Fast twitch, highly responsive to stimuli, fast action, muscle is light in color	– Slow twitch, less responsive, slow in action, muscle is dark in color
Skin	– Has the most skin pores of any race. – Better cooling – Most skin surface in relationship anatomy.	– Least pores – Inadequate cooling – Least
Nutrients	– Highest nutrient density (most vitamins, minerals and amino acids per square inch)	– Least

PARASYMPATHETIC SYSTEM
(Influenced by Pineal Glands response to Darkness)
The physical aspects influenced by Melanin's nighttime production

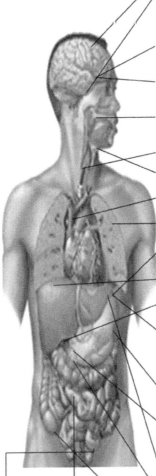

RIGHT BRAIN: intuitive and special capacities

HYPOTHALAMUS: anterior medial

POSTERIOR PITUITARY GLAND: produces two hormones, controls water, metabolism, blood pressure, kidney function, smooth muscle action.

PINEAL GLAND is responsive to light, reproductive cycles and pigmentation

PAROTID GLAND: stimulates parasympathetic organs and glands, regulates DNA material

PARATHYROIDS: parathoormone releases calcium from bones.

TONSILS: immune system organ; infection warning system

THYMUS: immune system organ
LUNGS: carbon dioxide, Oxygen and waste gases exchange from blood.

ADRENAL MEDULLA: creates norepinephrine, controls, tend and befriend.

LIVER: energy storage, food processing, detoxification, kwk

GALLBLADDER: bile storage
ADRENAL CORTEX: (outer) creates several hormones controls swelling, inflammation, sodium, potassium balanced, glucocoricoids, stimulates production of carbohydrates from proteins.

STOMACH: secretes hydrochloric acid for digestion

PANCREAS: stimulated by vagus nerve, creates digestive enzymes, carbohydrate metabolism and digestion of sugars, secretes insulin, glycogon

SPLEEN: immune system organ blood regulation and storage

DUODENUM: first part of small intestine, contains openings of pancreatic duct and absorption. Liver's gall bladder duct is attached to it

SMALL INTESTINE: digestion and absorption

LARGE INTESTINE: B vitamins manufactured, water absorbed

APPENDIX: immune system organ lymph gland, regulates blood cell production.

SYMPATHETIC SYSTEM
(Influence By Pineal Glands Response To Light)
The physical aspects influence by Melanin's daytime production

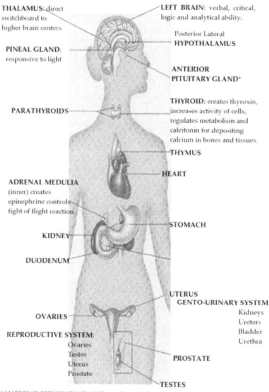

THALAMUS: direct switchboard to higher brain centers

LEFT BRAIN: verbal, critical, logic and analytical ability.

Posterior Lateral HYPOTHALAMUS

PINEAL GLAND: responsive to light

ANTERIOR PITUITARY GLAND*

PARATHYROIDS

THYROID: creates thyroxin, increases activity of cells, regulates metabolism and calcitonin for depositing calcium in bones and tissues.

THYMUS

HEART

ADRENAL MEDULLA (inner) creates epinephrine controls fight of flight reaction.

STOMACH

KIDNEY

DUODENUM

UTERUS
GENTO-URINARY SYSTEM
Kidneys
Ureters
Bladder
Urethra

OVARIES

REPRODUCTIVE SYSTEM:
Ovaries
Testes
Uterus
Prostate

PROSTATE

TESTES

*ANTERIOR PITUITARY GLAND: works with thyroid, adrenal and gonads, produces the following hormones:
1. **GH** (Growth Hormone): bone and general body growth, physical shape
2. **TSH** (Thyroid stimulating hormone) influences the formation and growth of thyroid gland
3. **ACTH** (adrenal cortex stimulating hormones): formation of adrenal cortex hormones
4. **LH, FSH, beta LPH**.

Arteries	Calcium Metabolism
Capillaries	Cardiovascular System
Ligaments, Connective Tissue	Muscle System
Neuromuscular System	Reproductive System
Skeletal System	Urinary System
Veins	

HUMAN DEVELOPMENT –SKIN LAYERS

Each race has a skin layer that is dominate. Black people's dominate skin is the Mesoderm and influences their life and chemistry.

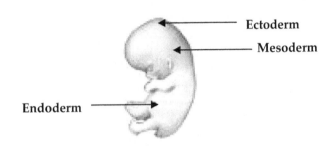

Types of Skin Layers
(Body parts and organs formed from Derma layers of skin)

Mesoderm
> Pineal (melanin), brain, spinal cord, heart, muscle, cartilage, kidney, sex organs, bones, lymph
> *Mesomorphic People=Africans*

Ectoderm
> Bladder, mouth, urethra, lens cornea, nasal cavity, skin
> *Ectomorphic People=Europeans*

Endoderm
> Liver, pancreas, lungs, thyroid
> *Endomorphic People=Asians*

Note: A disease to an organ or area affects all parts developed from that skin (derm) layer.

MELANIN'S REFLECTION ON THE FACE AND EMBRYO

The mesoderm layer is dominant in Black people. This is where the prefrontal cortex resides and emotions and intellect meet in a balance state.

EMBRYO   FACE   GESTATION
(Growth of unborn child)

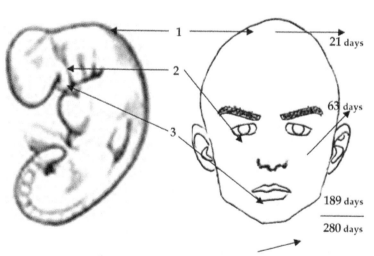

1. Ectoderm, 1st Trimester of prenatal growth
2. Mesoderm, 2nd Trimester of prenatal growth
3. Endoderm, 3rd trimester of prenatal growth

CHILDHOOD DEVELOPMENT

Fix Reaction Formative Behavior

Child	Adult
Cling to Mother	Hug (Greeting Form; when departing:
Root Nipple (breastfeeding)	Kissing cheeks, lips, derived from rooting nipple
"koo-ee" sounds	"oo"
(reward sound, joy sound)	("oo" it is nice to see you)
"Koo-ee" is a manipulative technique	

Bonding Before Birth

Fetus Sensors Bond	Complements or Synchronizes
– Taste	Movement of Eyes, Expressions, Body,
– Touch	Limbs, Breathing, Pulse, Temperature and
– Sight	Heart Rate are complementary and.or
– Smell	synchronized to mothers and father that is
– Hearing	bonded to mother physically, emotionally and spiritually. Synchronization is Melanin dependent.

The human body has one sense which is the melinated brain. The body has 5 sensors and 1 sense

Childhood Milestones

Trimester Developmen t	Behavioral Milestones	Tendency	Dysfunction Emotion
1st Trimester	Bond	Clinger/Avoider	Scary/Fear
	Retachment	Pursuing/Isolating	Anger
2nd Trimester	Identity	Controlling/Diffusing	Anxious
	Competence	Competitor/Manipulator	Embarrassment
3rd Trimester	Concern	Caretakers/Loners	Introvert/
	Intimacy	Rebel/Conformist	Extrovert (too happy)

If the mother is stressed, malnourished or consumes drugs then the child develops these emotions under the heading Dysfunction Emotion. Children and adults that exhibit these emotions in excess indicate the Trimester of stress and inability to develop a behavior indicated under Behavioral Milestones.

Emotional Vocabulary

Emotions and character logic similar to each zodiac sign
An emotional vocabulary is essential to bonding to self

BRAIN

The brain is Melanin dependent and uses Melanin in different forms.

Cerebrum Lobes (Sections)

LOBE	Nutrient/Hormone
Frontal	Tyrosine, Phenylalanine, Testosterone
Parietal	Acetylcholine, Lecithin, Estrogen
Temporal	GABA, Glutamine, Lipoic Acid, Progesterone
Occipital	Melatonin, Serotonin, DHEA, Pregnenolone, 5HTP (Tryptophane)

Malnourishment caused by eating junk foods, legal and illegal drugs and emotional and social stressors which results in inadequate nutrients to the brain and inadequate thinking. The brain develops thoughts and emotions that are False Positives sees structure (truth) where there is no truth and false negatives sees no structure (no design) where these is structure. See the truth as lies and the lies as truth. The mind becomes a conflict between thoughts and emotions and open to control by others (alien culture, white culture).

---

5 Actions (Variables)

Black people's Relationship Variables (influenced by Melanin)

*Social   *Economic   *Political
                 *Military   *Spiritual

Herbs
(Stimulate movements of Melanin)

Outward
Diaphoretic, expectorant, colds/flu

Inward
Liver, pancreas, digestion, seasonings

Upward
Astringents, stimulants

Downward
Diuretics, calmatives, laxatives

Immunity
Blood purifiers, infection, yeast

PSYCHOLOGY
(Difference between Black and White Races)

BLACK RACE (African-Centered Thought)	WHITE RACE (European-Centered Thought)
-Equally uses right and left hemisphere of brain and mid-brain. -Characterized by right-minded spiritual concepts, love, affection and sharing.	-Characterized by unhollistic Egotism, illogical use of left mind, non-spiritual individualism, rationalizations and non-creative.
-Mid-brain characterized by equal balances of rational thought and creative thought.	-Rationales based upon conflict between evil subconscious and good conscious. Military logic and predator nature.
-Time exists in "now" and is eternal and cyclic. Future, past and present are combined.	-No present tense of life. Life exists in the past and future; this results in time conflicts and places no value on present.
-Time is based on the beginning and ending of an event and is composed of the seen and unseen (spiritual, God manifested) causes of an event. Commonly called colored people's time. Time is fixed by the event. For example, the seasons of spring, summer, winter and fall, start according to nature's (unseen) clock.	-Time is a fixed abastract measurable duration. The seasons start according to a fixed calendar date and not according to nature.
-Thoughts are concept oriented. The meaning of thoughts as well as of words are based on the story (situations) they are used in,. For example, the word "bad" can be meant as good, modern intellectual, excellence or bad. Consequently, this gives rise to statements such as	-Thoughts are linear oriented. The meaning of words are fixed and based upon static logic rationales. Consequently, a "bad car" means a car unacceptable instead of the Anti-Centric meaning of an excellent car.

50

BLACK RACE (African-Centered Thought)	WHITE RACE (European-Centered Thought)
"That's a bad car".	
-Culture is based upon Maat, the family (extended) marriage, ancestors, harmony with nature, children not yet born, spirituality).	-Culture is based upon creating evil to control good and creating good to control evil.
-Communal, Family and child Centered.	-Have a pride-type family (similar to animals).
	-Control of nature.
	-Religions are political systems used to manipulate the powerless.
	-Self centered.
-Property owned by society; shared resources.	-Property is owned by individuals; No sharing of resources.
-Marriages: Predominately polygamous included polygyny and monogamous marriages, many marriages styles and types.	-Monogamous and the practice of polygamous relationships as sexual recreation (illegalgamy).
-Sex is reproductive, regenerational and spiritually used to serve Maat.	-Sex is a physical activity, recreational and reproductive.
-Individual's value in society is based upon what the individual contributes to society or "you are what you do"	-"You are what you Own".
-Economics. Abundantly sharing your goods, talent, labor, child rearing, and ancestors knowledge with society.	-Economics based upon scarcity, consumerism, or the creation of shortages. Thus, only an elite few can gain access to goods, talent and knowledge, human and natural resources.
-Science is whollistic and controlled by MAAT.	-Science is rational and abstract based upon one group (the elite) controlling a

BLACK RACE (African-Centered Thought)	WHITE RACE (European-Centered Thought)
	system.
-Religion. Monotheism (belief in one God) Do Not Fear God.	-Belief in many Gods. God created the Devil. (Evil type God). You Fear God.
-A person is born to achieve their highest level of humanism.	-A person is born in sin.
-Life is based on sense (seen) and nonsense (unseen) and is beyond the power of the mind.	-Life based upon seen, measured, objective or abstracted knowledge.
-Humans belong to God (no slavery).	-Humans can be owned by man (Full Slavery).
Psychology based upon moving torwards, away from and/or with an idea/emotion.	Psychology based upon Greek fairy tale Oedipus Myth.
People can be emotionally and/or spiritually ill.	People can only be mentally (rationally) ill.
Emotions adapt to each other.	Good emotions are constantly at war with bad emotions (primitive animal feelings).

MELANIN CONVERSIONS/MELANIN CHANGING FORM

> Phenylalanine changes to Epinephrine in a
> progression of steps (Adrenaline)

Phenylalanine→→→Tyrosine→→→DOPA
(Dihydroxyphenylalamine) →→→Dopamine→→→
Norepinephrine (Noradrenaline)→→→Epinephrine
(Adrenaline)

> Tryptophan changes to Melanin

Tryptophan→→→Serotonin →→→MSH (Melanin Stimulating
Hormone) →→→ Melanocytes→→→Melanin

Each Melanocyte controls 36 to 40 cells.

MELANIN (PINEAL) NUTRITION

Melanin is the foundation for immunity. It is a free radical scavenger; aids digestion, antioxidant, bones, nerves, cellular and hormone functions. The following are essential for melanin production.

MELANIN HORMONES: NERVOUS SYSTEM STIMULATED:	Serotonin/ Sympathetic Stress	Melatonin Parasympathetic Stress
	SUPPLEMENTS	
	Vitamin A	d-Alpha Tocopherol
	B-6	B-1
	B-12	B-2
	Calcium	Magnesium
	Chromium	Vanadium
	Cobalamin	Coenzyme Q-10
	Copper	Vitamin E
	Vitamin C	Vitamin D, Iodine
	Niacin	Niacinamide
	Serotonin Sympathetic Stress	**Melatonin Parasympathetic Stress**
	Folic Acid	Folic Acid
	Manganese	Manganese
	Potasium	Panthothenic Acid
	Riboflavin	Phosphorous
	Silica	Pyridoxal 5 Phosphate
	Selenium	Riboflavin
	Bromelain	Choline
	Iron	Zinc
	Chondrotin Sulfate	Glucosamine Sulfate
	Tablets/Liquid Serotonin	Tablets/Liquid Melatonin
HERBS	*Combine:*	*Combine:*
	Gingko or Gotu kola Damiana, Eybright Echinacea	Gingko or Gotu Kola, Chamomile, Echinacea
AMINO ACIDS		
	Ormithine, Arginine SULFUR AMINO ACIDS Methionine, Cysteine, Taurine	Phenylalanine, Tyrosine ALKALINE AMINO ACID Histidine, Lysine, Glycine

ACID AMINO ACIDS	
Glutamic Acid, Aspartic	Glutamine

GLANDULARS	
Pancreas, Liver Brain	Pancreas, Pitutiary, Adrenal, Brain

See How to Measure Melanin to identify the herbs needed for over stimulated serotonin and melatonin over use.

PINEAL NUTRITION

Serotonin Sympathetic Stress	Melatonin/ Parasympathetic Stress
Herbs	
Combination Gingko or Gotu Kola Damiana, Eybright Echinacea	Combination: Gingko or Gotu Kola Chamomile, Echinacea

Formula
Saw Palmetto, Black Cohosh, Fo-Ti, Gingko, Lobelia, Eyebright, Burdock, Dandelion Root, Alfalfa
Foods
Apricots, Apples, Peaches, Mangoes, Papayas, Star Fruit, Figs, Dates, Bananas, Plantains, Yams, Red Cherries, Blue Grapes, Guava, Broccoli, Spelt, Wild Rice, Blueberries, Collard Greens, Cauliflower, Oranges, Dandelion Greens, Fresh Olives, Raw Peanuts, Strawberries, Currants, Lemons, Turnips, Soybeans.
Food Classification ➤ Carbohydrates increase Tryptophan-Calmness (melatonin) ➤ Protein Increases Dopamine/Norepinephrine/Tyrosine =Alertness (Serotonin) ➤ Fruits stimulate melanin energy ➤ Vegetables stabilize melanin energy

BLACK PEOPLE'S SLEEP PATTERN

Steps	Electrical/Magnetic
1. Male principle	Decrease in electricity
Female Principle	Increase in Magnetism
2. Male Principle	Generates magnetism, regenerates
Female Principle	Electricity regenerates magnetism,
3. Third Eye/Pineal	Generates electricity electromagnetic
Gland	balanced vibrations

Steps   Sensations

1. Holistic pictures of spirit and physical life.
2. Feel earth, lunar, solar and galaxy cycles.
3. Emotional movement in body, psyche dream trance.
4. Dream about life in timeless state
5. REM –Pineal Gland Vibrations.
6. Reverse Order (Steps 5,4,3, 2, 1) and returns to physical body existence.

AFRICAN SLEEP

Sleep is the Inactivity of the Conscious Mind.
Rest is the Inactivity of the Body

ENTER SLEEP				EXIT SLEEP		
Body	Mind	Spirit	Black Dot	Spirit	Mind	Body
Inactive	Voluntary Inactive	Voluntary Active	Enter-Exit	Voluntary Inactive Involuntary Active	Voluntary Active	Active

CYCLIC SLEEP SEQUENCE

CYCLES			
Earth	Lunar	Solar	Celestial
Physical Inactive	Conscious Emotion, Inactivity	Electrical Decrease See Pictures	Magnetic Increase Floating

SLEEP SUPPLEMENTS			
Calcium	3,000 mg	Magnesium	1,500 mg
Vitamin B Complex	100 mg	Vitamin B6 (Pyridoxine)	300 mg
Vitamin B5 (Panthonenic Acid)	300 mg	Melatonin	1 – 3 mcg
GABA	As Directed	Nutritional Brewer's Yeast	3 tbsp

HERBS
Catnip, Passion Flower, Hops, Skullcap, Chamomile, Lady's Slipper, Valerian, Kava Kava

MELANIN ENERGY CLASSIFICATION

These are various chemical and mental processes stimulated by melanin's serotonin and melatonin

The Male Principle (Serotonin)	The Female Principle (Melatonin)
Go	Stop
Sympathetic	Parasympathetic
Acid (Fast moving)	Alkaline (slow moving)
Vertical	Horizontal
Destruction	Construction
Catabolic	Anabolic
Anaerobic	Aerobic
Systolic	Diasytolic
Melanin insufficient	Melanin deficient
High specific gravity	Low specific gravity
Hemolyzed	Non-hemolyzed
Action	Relaxation
Future	Past
Left Brain	Right Brain
Lower jaw	Upper Jaw
Incisors	Molars
Think 1st, feel 2nd	Feel 1st, think 2nd
Contraction	Expansion
Constipation	Diarrhea
Insulin	Glucogon
Carbohydrates	Fats
Urine	Saliva enzymes
Bright colors	Dark colors
Objective	Subjective
High turbidity	Low turbidity
High pulse	Low pulse
Science	Art
Vagina	Penis
Fight/Flight	Tend/BeFriend
Oxidant (oxidize)	Antioxidant
Realistic	Idealistic
Analytical	Harmonizer

MELANINE HORMONE SYMPTOMS

Excess stimulation of Serotonin and Melatonin has these symptoms

Serotonin/Sympathetic Stress	Melatonin/Parasympathetic Stress
Dry mouth	Saliva and tear quality increased
Eyes set inward	Eyes set outward; exophthalmos with irritation of cranial nerve III (e.g. form exophthalmic)
Fat energy uses decrease	Fat energy usage increase
Glucose energy increased (insulin)	Glucose energy decreased (or increased)
WBC decreased	WBC increased
Constipation	Normal/Diarrhea
Poor circulation associated with vasoconstriction	Poor circulation associated with decreased pulse pressure
Heart; kidney; BP problems	Heart problems
Indigestion; ulcers; gall bladder; and bowel problems	Indigestion; ulcers; bowel problems; colitis
Food allergies	Allergies; asthma
Immunity low	Immunity high
Increased thyroid activity	Decreased thyroid activity
Male principle	Female principle
Pupil large	Pupil small
Increase sensory perception	Decrease sensory perception
Pulse increased; arrhythmia	Pulse decrease
Respiratory rate decrease or increase; Bronchial dilation; respiratory depth increased	Respiratory rate decrease or increase; Bronchial constriction
Systolic BP and pulse	When standing, failure of systolic

pressure increased	BP and pulse pressure
Urine specific gravity high	Urine specific gravity low
Urination decreased	Urination increase
Temperature increased	Temperature decreased

MELANIN HORMONE SYMPTOMS

Serotonin/Sympathetic Stress	Melatonin/Parasympathetic Stress
Cold sweat on hands, or cold dry hands	Hands warm and dry
Nervous tensions; tremors	Nervous tension; depression; anxiety
Vasoconstriction	Vasodilation
Breathing increase	Breathing decrease
Penis Flaccid	Penis erect
Digestion decrease	Digestion increase
Sexual desire decrease	Sexual desire increase
Sleep decrease (sleepless)	Sleep increase (sleep decrease)
Aggressive	Passive
Serotonin high	Serotonin low
Melatonin low	Melatonin High
Rheumatism	Arthritis
High energy	Low energy
Colors: red, yellow, orange	Colors: blue, indigo, violet
Decrease blood to skin	Increase blood to skin
Mania	Depression
Decrease progesterone	Increase progesterone
Testosterone	Estrogen
Increased during night	Increased during day

12 MELANIN CLUSTERS (CHAKRAS)

Melanin energy pathways are erroneously label Acupuncture Meridians. These meridians collide (cluster) in areas of the body. This results in 12 Melanin Clusters which are erroneously labeled Chakras. Only Melanin Dominate Black people have 12 clusters, other races have less. The clusters can be stimulated by hand, biomagnetics and Acupuncture needles. The stimulation can cause wellness and help with diseases.

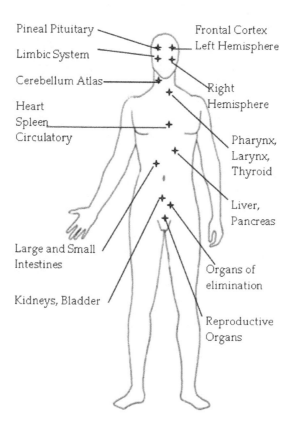

Pineal Pituitary

Limbic System

Cerebellum Atlas

Heart
Spleen
Circulatory

Large and Small
Intestines

Kidneys, Bladder

Frontal Cortex
Left Hemisphere

Right
Hemisphere

Pharynx,
Larynx,
Thyroid

Liver,
Pancreas

Organs of
elimination

Reproductive
Organs

MELANIN COLORS OF ZODIAC HOLISTIC CHART

BODY	ZODIAC	MUSIC NOTE	MELANIN COLORS	ZODIAC HOUSE
Pitiutary, Eyes, cerebrum, Nose	Aries	D	Red	1
Neck, Cerebellium, throat, Lower Brain, Thyroid	Taurus	E	Yellow	2
Heart, Thymus, Spleen	Leo	A	Orange	5
Kidney, Adrenal, Bladder	Libra	D	Yellow	7
Breast, Veins, Arteries, Stomach	Cancer	B	Green	4
Intestine, Liver, Pancreas, Lower Abdomen	Virgo	C	Violet	6
Sciatic Nerve, Thigh, Hips, Buttocks	Sagittarius	F	Purple	9
Genitals, Gonads, Rectum	Scorpio	E	Red	8
Para-thyroid, lower Leg, Colon, Ankles	Aquarius	A	Indigo	11
Feet, Circulation, Pineal	Pisces	B	Indigo	12
Knees, Teeth, Bones	Capricorn	G	Blue	10
Arms, Fallopian tubes, Thymus	Gemini	F	Violet	3

WHOLISTIC CHART

This Chart relates melanin clusters to Melanin colors and other holistic aspects

Melanin Clusters	Glands	Kenetic Word	Colors	Music Note	Number Sound & Shape	Letters Sounds & Shapes
Third Eye	Pineal	IKH	Indigo	B	6	F O X
Crown	Pituitary	Mer	Violet	A	7	G Y P
Throat	Thyroid	Sekhem	Blue	G	5	E N W
Heart	Thymus	Kheper	Green	F	4	D M U
Solar Plex	Adrenal, Liver	AB	Yellow	E	3,8	C L U, H Q Z
Genital	Ovary, Testicle	Tekh	Orange	D	2,9	B K T, I R
Preineum	No Gland Colon, Rectum	Sefekht	Red	C	1	A J S

SUGGESTED READING

Afrika, Llaila: African Holistic Health

Barnes, Carol: Melanin: The Chemical key to Black greatness

Barr, F. E. " Melanin The Organizing Molecule" Medical Hypothesis Vol II:I March 1983

Boyd, William: Genetics and the Races of Man

Coon, C.S.: The Races of Europe

Gan, E.V. Lam K.M. "Oxidizing and Reducing Properties of Melanins" British Journal of Dermatology 8b (25) 1977

Hawley Gessner, G: The Condensed Chemical Dictionary

Kaidbey, Khet: Photoprotection by Melanin A Comparison of Black and Caucasian Skia J. American Acad Dermatol Vol 1 (34) Sept 1979

King, Richard: Black Dot (Humanities, Ancestral Blackness, The Black)

Loeb, Stanley: Nursing, 2007 drug Handbook

McGinness, J Proctor P: The Importance of the Fact that Melanin is Black J. Theor Biol Vol 39, pp 677-678

Morrison, W.L. "What is the Function of Melanin?" Arch Dermatol, Vol 121, pp 1160-1163 Sept. 1985

Price, Weston: Nutrition and Physical Degeneration

Prodor, P.H. Hilton, J.G., and McGinness J.E: Meeting on Biophysics and Biological Function of Melanins Pharma, 3-4, March 1980

Quay, W.B. Pineal Chemistry
Charles Thomas, Springfield, Ill 1974

Salazar, M.M. "Significance of the Interaction of Drug-Binding to Melanin Biochemical Pharmacology, Vol 28 pp 1181-1187, 1979

Thomas Clayton: Tabers Cyclopedic Medical Dictionary

Vaugh, G.M. "Melatonin in humans In Pineal Research Review Vol 2, pp 141-201 Alan R Liss Inc New York, NY 1984

Welsing, Francis: The Cress Theory (Racial Confrontation)

Williams, Richard: Textbook of Black-Related Diseases

ABOUT THE AUTHOR

Llaila O. Afrika is a Doctor of Naturopathy, Licensed "Acupuncturist", Licensed Medical Massage Therapist, Certified Addictionologist (treats all types of addiction), Certified Nutritional Counselor, Medical Astrologist, Spiritual Counselor, Marriage Counselor, Psychotherapist and worked as a nurse in the military. He has treated people of all races for diseases and has lectured in North and South America, Europe and Africa. He has been a leading pioneer in the African Science field and has books such as *African Holistic Health* (been on Essence Magazine Bestseller List for over ten years and is the largest selling book of its kind), *Nutricide*, a book about harmful drugs and foods that Black people consume, How to Raise Healthy Black Children (infancy to teenagers), a comprehensive text on parenting, children's behavior, growth, emotions, diseases and healthy foods and a history book title *The Gullah*.

Llaila has a line of specialty disease remedy Supplements.
To order DVD's, and CDs visit:
www.blackbookplus.com

Made in the USA
Coppell, TX
04 November 2020

40772260R00039